SIMPLIFYING FRACTIONS AND DECIMALS

through the Unifact method makes all the basic fraction and decimal operations easy. In small, concise steps it covers: types of fractions, rewriting improper fractions and mixed forms, rewriting fractions in simplest forms, multiplying and dividing fractions and decimals, adding and subtracting and cancelling.

SIMPLIFYING FRACTIONS AND DECIMALS
THE MOST EFFECTIVE WAY YET DEVISED
FOR LEARNING FRACTIONS AND DECIMALS!

SIMPLIFYING FRACTIONS AND DECIMALS

BY BRADLEY V. SMITH

A UNIFACT BOOK

A PROGRAMMED TEXT

BANTAM BOOKS
TORONTO · NEW YORK · LONDON

SIMPLIFYING FRACTIONS AND DECIMALS
Bantam Unifact edition published November 1966

Bantam Books are published by Bantam Books, Inc., a subsidiary
of Grosset & Dunlap, Inc. Its trade-mark, consisting of the words
"Bantam Books" and the portrayal of a bantam, is registered in the
United States Patent Office and in other countries. Marca Registrada.
Bantam Books, Inc., 271 Madison Avenue, New York, N.Y. 10016.

PRINTED IN THE UNITED STATES OF AMERICA

CONTENTS

TO THE READER

Learning is easiest when it is acquired in small increments . . . and reinforced by repetition.

This text develops the essentials of fraction and decimal theory in small, concise steps. Each frame contains a single idea. Each new idea is followed by an example. Each example is reinforced by a quiz question.

Explanations are simple and compact, enabling you to keep the key idea in sharp focus. Key ideas are purposely repeated. Each repetition, in turn, develops an expansion of the initial concept.

Learning is further reinforced by the text's self-quiz structure. Spot Checks, following each new discussion, repeat the text material and give the reader a quick report on his progress. To the reader who has followed the text, step by step, the answers to the Spot Check questions are obvious. This obviousness is an indication of successful learning . . . of new information and concepts acquired without conscious effort.

The Spot Checks are also progress reports. Each question is keyed to the frame which explains the idea the question checks. Thus, any weakness the quiz discloses can be instantly remedied.

Practice Exercises, spotted throughout the book, cover in sequence every major idea developed earlier in the text. If you can answer correctly every question in the Practice Exercises, you can be sure you have learned everything this book has to teach.

Answers to the Spot Checks and Practice Exercises will always be found on the following lefthand page.

ACKNOWLEDGMENTS

For review of the manuscript of this text, and for many helpful suggestions and addenda, the author is immensely grateful to Mr. Bryan Bunch, Chief Mathematics Editor, Harcourt, Brace and World, Inc., Mr. Raymond Walsh, Director of Mathematics, Westport Public School System, Westport, Connecticut and Mrs. Roberta Gleit, General Instructor, P.S. 13, Yonkers, N. Y. The author is also indebted to Mr. Fred W. Kautz, Mather Junior High School, Darien, Connecticut, who painstakingly checked all computations in both text and exercises.

PREFACE

Any writer on elementary mathematics is faced with a choice between explanations in familiar language, using terms that have been in common use for several generations, and explanations that have greater mathematical exactness but are not meaningful to a reader unschooled in the vocabulary. For example, in times past the term *number* was often used in places where a more rigorous practice would require *numeral*. In today's usage *number* refers to a concept rather than the variety of forms in which that concept can be expressed or named. Thus the number *two* can be variously written as Arabic 2, Roman II, Chinese and Japanese = ; or it can be given such fraction names as $\frac{4}{2}$, $\frac{8}{4}$, $\frac{10}{5}$. Modern practice distinguishes number, numeral, and name. A number is a concept of a certain type, regardless of the way it is symbolized or named. A number name is any of a variety of forms in which a given number concept can be expressed; a numeral is a symbol or group of symbols used to indicate a number or a part of a number.

Another example is the terminology now applied to expressions of the form $2\frac{1}{3}$, $5\frac{1}{2}$, $16\frac{3}{5}$. In times past these were called *mixed numbers*. But obviously it is not the numbers that are mixed, but the form of expression: specifically, fractional forms and integers. In the newer terminology they are *mixed forms*, not mixed numbers.

Much is to be said for this increase in mathematical rigor, much of which reflects the influence of recent curriculum studies in mathematics, particularly those prepared under the supervision of the Panel on Elementary School Mathematics of the School Mathematics Study Group. Yet on the debit side is the fact that much of the new terminology and many of the new forms of definition and demonstration increase the difficulty of making simple those areas of applied mathematics where many students have already been troubled, and where readers familiar with an older terminology are likely to compound their confusion.

The aim of this book is to simplify explanations, to make learning as easy as possible . . . but without sacrifice of mathematical exactness. For this reason the new terminology has been used side by side with the old. The reader is introduced gradually to the methods and vocabulary of the new mathematics, but without sacrifice of the guide-posts that make what is new and important intelligible in terms that are familiar.

B.V.S.

HOW TO USE THIS UNIFACT TEXT

i. Where should we begin?

With Frame No. 1.

---

ii. But Frame No. 1 is obvious. Can't we skip to some place where the going gets tough?

No.

---

iii. Why not?

Because if we read every frame carefully, the going will never get tough.

---

iv. But isn't it tiresome to read what we already know?

The purpose of this book is not to entertain but to teach us to use fractions and decimals efficiently—and to do this simply, directly, and painlessly.

---

v. After reading the first frame, what next?

Continue to the first Spot Check. Don't skip.

---

vi. How are the Spot Checks to be used?

Try to answer every question correctly. Fill in the blanks (or write answers on a separate sheet of paper), then check all answers against the text answers (which are printed on the next left-hand page).

vii. What if some of our answers are wrong?

Return to the frame indicated opposite each Spot Check question missed. The frame will tell us what we did wrong.

viii. When can we move on to a new section?

When we have been able to answer every question correctly in the preceding Spot Check.

ix. Is it necessary to progress so slowly?

Learning is easy if we learn one fact at a time—and learn it thoroughly—before moving on to the next. We make the greatest progress slowly —with constant repetition of key ideas. This is the psychological basis of the UNIFACT method.

x. Doesn't the text contain many repetitions?

It does. The repetitions have been carefully planned and tested.

xi. **Why?**

> Because repetitions emphasize a fact and fix it in the mind. Repetitions are the key to efficient learning.

xii. **How about the Practice Exercises? If we understand the principle they illustrate, can't we skip them and go on to the next subject?**

> The answer: no! The exercises are both a check on our progress and an effective device to deepen learning. Repetition of operations reinforces what we have already learned.

xiii. **What is an average score for the exercises?**

> 100%. If our score is less than 100% in any section, we should turn back a few pages and reread the section.

xiv. **Summarizing: What are the basic rules for using this text?**

> 1. Don't skip.
> 2. Read every frame.
> 3. Master every question in every Spot Check.
> 4. Work every problem in every Practice Exercise.

xv. **What can we expect as a result?**

> To acquire easily—with minimum effort—a thorough understanding of basic operations with fractions and decimals.

FRACTIONS

1. If any object is cut into two equal parts, what do we call each part?

    A half.

2. If any object is cut into three equal parts, what do we call each part?

    A third.

3. If any object is cut into five equal parts, what do we call each part?

    A fifth.

4. Write "one half" in mathematical notation.

    $\frac{1}{2}$.

5. Write "two halves" in mathematical notation.

    $\frac{2}{2}$.

6. Write "one third" and "one fifth" in mathematical notation.

    $\frac{1}{3}$, $\frac{1}{5}$.

7. **What is the general term for expressions in this form?**

   Fractions; or, more specifically, fraction names.

---

8. **In a fraction what do we call the numeral written above the line?**

   The numerator.

---

9. **What name is given to the numeral written below the line?**

   The denominator.

---

10. **In the expression $\frac{3}{5}$, which numeral is the numerator?**

    3.

---

11. **In the expression $\frac{3}{5}$, which numeral is the denominator?**

    5.

---

12. **If you wanted to indicate that 3 is to be divided by five, you could write $3 \div 5$. Is there any other way?**

    Yes. You could write $\frac{3}{5}$.

---

13. **If you wanted to indicate that 2 is to be divided by 3, you could write 2 ÷ 3. Is there any other way?**

    Yes. You could write $\frac{2}{3}$.

14. **How do we determine that if 1 unit is divided into 2 equal parts, each part is $\frac{1}{2}$ the unit?**

    We divide 1 by 2.

15. **What do these three facts tell us about fractions?**

    That a fraction is an expression showing a division to be performed.

16. **What then does the denominator represent?**

    A divisor (a number used to divide another).

17. **What does the numerator represent?**

    A dividend (the number to be divided).

18. **If the division were performed, what would we call the answer?**

    A quotient.

19. **Putting all these facts together, what do we learn about the nature of a fraction?**

    That a fraction is an indicated quotient.

1. Two halves are equal to _____.

_____[1]

2. A third represents one part of an object that has been cut into _____ equal parts.

_____[2]

3. If something has been cut into _____ equal parts, each part represents a fifth.

_____[3]

4. $\frac{1}{2}$ is called "_____."

_____[4]

5. The expression $\frac{2}{2}$ represents "_____."

_____[5]

6. $\frac{1}{3}$ and $\frac{1}{5}$ are symbols, respectively, for "_____" and "_____."

_____[6]

7. The general name for expressions of the form $\frac{1}{2}$, $\frac{1}{3}$, $\frac{2}{3}$, $\frac{3}{5}$, etc., is _____.

_____[7]

8. The *numerator* is the name given to that part of a fraction written _____ the line.

_____[8]

9. The _____ is the name given to that part of a fraction written below the line.

_____[9]

10. In the expression $\frac{3}{5}$, what part of the fraction is represented by 3? _____.

_____[10]

11. 5 is the _____ of the fraction $\frac{3}{5}$.

_____[11]

12. The expression $\frac{3}{5}$ is used to indicate that 3 is to be _____ by 5.

_____[12]

13. If we wanted to indicate that 2 is to be _____ by 3, we could symbolize the operation by 2 _____3.

_____[13]

14. To find $\frac{1}{3}$ of 1 unit, we _____ 1 by 3.

_____[14]

15. Generalizing from these examples, we can say that a fraction is an expression indicating that a _____ is to be performed.

_____[15]

16. A denominator, thus, is actually a _____.

_____[16]

17. The dividend is represented by the _____.

_____[17]

18. A *quotient* is the name given to the result of a _____.

_____[18]

19. It follows, then, that a fraction is an indicated _____.

_____[19]

TYPES OF FRACTIONS

20. What name is usually given to fractions such as $\frac{1}{2}$, $\frac{1}{3}$, $\frac{2}{3}$, $\frac{4}{5}$, etc.?

Common fractions.

---

21. What is the definition of a common fraction?

A fraction whose numerator and denominator are both integers (whole numbers).

---

22. Is $\frac{57}{129}$ a common fraction?

Yes.

---

23. Why?

Because both 57 and 129 are integers.

---

24. Is $\frac{\frac{1}{2}}{5}$ a common fraction?

No, because the numerator, $\frac{1}{2}$, is not an integer.

---

25. What do we call fractions such as $\frac{\frac{1}{2}}{5}$, $\frac{3}{\frac{1}{4}}$, and $\frac{\frac{1}{3}}{\frac{1}{2}}$?

Complex fractions.

---

1. A whole (or one)
2. Three
3. Five
4. One half
5. Two halves
6. One third; one fifth
7. Fractions
8. Above
9. Denominator
10. The numerator
11. Denominator
12. Divided
13. Divided; ÷
14. Divide
15. Division
16. Divisor
17. Numerator
18. Division
19. Quotient

---

26. What is the definition of a complex fraction?

A fraction in which either the numerator or denominator contains a fraction, or both contain fractions.

---

27. Are all common fractions of the same type?

No. There are two types of common fractions, *proper* fractions and *improper* fractions.

---

28. What is a proper fraction?

A fraction in which the numerator is smaller than the denominator.

---

29. Give some examples of proper fractions.

$\frac{1}{2}$, $\frac{1}{3}$, $\frac{2}{3}$, $\frac{7}{8}$, $\frac{19}{21}$, $\frac{121}{139}$.

---

30. What is an improper fraction?

A fraction in which the numerator is equal to or greater than the denominator.

---

31. Give some examples of improper fractions.

$\frac{2}{2}, \quad \frac{3}{2}, \quad \frac{4}{3}, \quad \frac{7}{5}, \quad \frac{21}{15}, \quad \frac{182}{16}.$

32. If the numerator of a fraction is greater than the denominator, what other fact is implied?

That the value of the fraction is greater than 1. Thus

$$\frac{3}{2} = 1\frac{1}{2}$$
$$\frac{4}{3} = 1\frac{1}{3}$$
$$\frac{7}{3} = 2\frac{1}{3}$$

etc.

33. Is there a special name for forms such as $1\frac{1}{2}$, $1\frac{1}{3}$, $1\frac{2}{5}$, $7\frac{3}{4}$, $23\frac{15}{16}$, etc.?

Yes. Mixed forms (or mixed numbers).

34. What is the definition of a mixed form?

An expression consisting of the symbol for an integer (whole number) plus a fraction (more precisely, the sum of an integer and a fraction).

35. What does a mixed form such as $1\frac{2}{3}$ represent?

The sum of the integer and the number represented by the fraction. Thus

$$1\frac{2}{3} = 1 + \frac{2}{3}$$

1. What is a common fraction? _____

   _____ [21]

2. Are $\frac{1}{2}$, $\frac{2}{7}$, $\frac{5}{9}$ common fractions? _____

   _____ [20]

3. Is $\frac{27}{559}$ a common fraction? _____

   _____ [22]

4. Give the reason you think $\frac{27}{559}$ is or is not a common

   fraction. _____

   _____ [23]

5. Is $\frac{1}{2}$ an integer (whole number)? _____

   _____ [24]

6. Give an example of a fraction that is not a common

   fraction. _____

   _____ [24]

7. Give an example of a complex fraction. _____

   _____ [25]

8. What name is given to fractions either the numerator
   or denominator of which is not a whole number
   (integer), or in which both are not whole numbers

   (integers)? _____

   _____ [26]

9. Proper fractions and improper fractions are two types

   of _____ fractions.

   _____ [27]

10. A fraction whose numerator is smaller than the denominator (EXAMPLE: $\frac{2}{3}$) is called a _____ fraction.

_____[28]

11. $\frac{121}{139}$ and $\frac{789}{790}$ are both examples of _____ fractions.

_____[29]

12. Why? _____

_____[28]

13. If the numerator of a fraction is equal to or greater than the denominator, the fraction is called

_____.

_____[30]

14. $\frac{16}{17}$ and $\frac{18}{17}$ are, respectively, _____ and _____ fractions.

_____[29, 31]

15. Every improper fraction has a value equal to or greater than _____.

_____[32]

16. What is a mixed form? _____

_____[34]

17. Give three examples of mixed forms.

_____[33]

1. A fraction whose numerator and denominator are both integers (whole numbers).
2. Yes.
3. Yes.
4. It is a common fraction because both 27 and 559 are integers (whole numbers).
5. No. $\frac{1}{2}$ is a fraction.
6. $\frac{\frac{1}{2}}{5}$ (or any other expression in which a fraction occurs in the numerator, denominator, or both).
7. $\frac{\frac{1}{2}}{5}$ (or a similar expression, as noted above).
8. Complex fraction.
9. Common.
10. Proper.
11. Proper.
12. Because in both cases the numerator is smaller than the denominator.
13. An improper fraction.
14. Proper; improper.
15. 1.
16. An expression consisting of an integer plus a fraction.
17. $1\frac{1}{8}$, $1\frac{2}{5}$, $1\frac{3}{4}$ (or other expressions of similar form).

Practice Exercise 1: Types of Fractions and Fractional Expressions

Using the symbols P, for proper fraction; I, for improper fraction; C, for complex fraction; and M, for mixed form, identify the following expressions:

1. $\frac{2}{9}$

2. $\frac{8}{9}$

3. $\frac{9}{9}$

4. $1\frac{1}{7}$

5. $\frac{2}{\frac{1}{3}}$

6. $\frac{129}{127}$

7. $\frac{879}{880}$

8. $880\frac{1}{879}$

9. $\frac{3}{\frac{1}{879}}$

10. $\frac{7}{7}$

11. $\frac{100234}{100234}$

12. $\frac{1132}{159}$

13. $2229\frac{11}{16}$

14. $\frac{120089}{\frac{21}{59}}$

15. $\frac{\frac{10}{13}}{51}$

1.	P	9.	C
2.	P	10.	I
3.	I	11.	I
4.	M	12.	I
5.	C	13.	M
6.	I	14.	C
7.	P	15.	C
8.	M		

REWRITING IMPROPER FRACTIONS AND MIXED FORMS

36. Can every improper fraction be expressed as a mixed form?

Yes, unless the denominator is an exact divisor of the numerator (EXAMPLE: $\frac{4}{2} = 2$), in which case the result will be a whole number (rather than a whole number plus a fraction). Thus

$$\frac{4}{2} = 2$$
$$\frac{5}{2} = 2\frac{1}{2}$$

37. Write $\frac{6}{5}$ as a mixed form.

$1\frac{1}{5}$.

38. Write $\frac{17}{15}$ as a mixed form.

$1\frac{2}{15}$.

39. Write $\frac{34}{15}$ as a mixed form.

$2\frac{4}{15}$.

---

40. From the above examples derive a general rule for rewriting an improper fraction as a whole number or mixed form.

RULE: Perform the indicated division; that is, divide the numerator of the fraction by the denominator. The answer will be a whole number plus a fraction (the remainder).

---

41. Does the reverse operation hold: Can every mixed form be expressed as an improper fraction?

Yes.

---

42. Express $1\frac{1}{2}$ as an improper fraction.

$\frac{(2 \times 1) + 1}{2} = \frac{3}{2}$.

---

43. Express $2\frac{3}{5}$ as an improper fraction.

$\frac{(5 \times 2) + 3}{5} = \frac{13}{5}$.

---

44. Express $15\frac{2}{3}$ as an improper fraction.

$\frac{(3 \times 15) + 2}{3} = \frac{47}{3}$.

---

45. From the above examples, derive a general rule for expressing a mixed form as an improper fraction.

> RULE: To express a mixed form as an improper fraction, multiply the whole number by the denominator of the fraction and add the numerator of the fraction to this product. The sum is placed over the original denominator.

46. When are improper fractions rewritten as mixed forms or as integers?

> When rewriting results in more convenient units. For example: If the answer to a problem relating to gasoline is $\frac{76}{8}$ gallons, we would reduce the answer to $9\frac{1}{2}$ gallons. It is easier to visualize quantities of gasoline in terms of gallons rather than in terms of $\frac{1}{8}$ gallons. Similarly, most quantities are sold or thought of in terms of the largest convenient unit of measure.

47. Why are mixed forms often rewritten as improper fractions?

> For simplicity in computation. As we will see later (in the sections on adding, subtracting, multiplying, and dividing fractions), it is often easier to perform operations on mixed forms (such as dividing $21\frac{11}{16}$ by $8\frac{2}{3}$) when the mixed forms are written as common fractions.

1. Every _____ can be expressed as either an integer or a mixed form.

   _____[36]

2. $\frac{10}{9}$ is a(n) _____ fraction.

   _____[37–39]

3. If the numerator of a fraction is larger than the denominator, and we perform the indicated division (that is, divide the numerator by the denominator),

   the result will be a _____ number or a

   _____ number plus a fraction.

   _____[40]

4. An expression consisting of a whole number plus a

   fraction is called a _____ form.

   _____[36, 40]

5. Every mixed form can be expressed as a(n) _____
   fraction.

   _____[41]

6. To express a mixed form as a(n) _____ fraction,

   multiply the whole number by the _____ of the

   fraction and add the _____ of the fraction
   to this product. The resulting sum is placed over the

   _____ of the fraction.

   _____[45]

7. $\frac{76}{8}$ gallons of gasoline can be visualized more easily if we express the quantity as _____ gallons.

———————————————————————————[46]

8. In computations with mixed forms the operations are often easier if the mixed forms are expressed as

————————————————————————————.

———————————————————————————[47]

Practice Exercise 2: Improper Fractions and Mixed Forms

Rewrite the following fractions as whole numbers or mixed forms.

1. $\frac{10}{5}$

2. $\frac{31}{20}$

3. $\frac{65}{20}$

4. $\frac{45}{8}$

5. $\frac{33}{9}$

6. $\frac{36}{4}$

7. $\frac{26}{3}$

8. $\frac{100}{10}$

Rewrite the following mixed forms as improper fractions.

9. $1\frac{1}{5}$

10. $3\frac{2}{7}$

11. $4\frac{1}{2}$

12. $8\frac{7}{15}$

13. $2\frac{11}{20}$

14. $4\frac{3}{10}$

15. $5\frac{1}{6}$

16. $2\frac{5}{24}$

1. Improper fraction
2. Improper
3. Whole; whole
4. Mixed
5. Improper

6. Improper; denominator; numerator; denominator
7. $9\frac{1}{2}$
8. Improper fractions

ANSWERS: PRACTICE EXERCISE 2

1. 2
2. $1\frac{11}{20}$
3. $3\frac{5}{20}$
4. $5\frac{5}{8}$

5. $3\frac{6}{9}$
6. 9
7. $8\frac{2}{3}$
8. 10

9. $\frac{6}{5}$
10. $\frac{23}{7}$
11. $\frac{9}{2}$
12. $\frac{127}{15}$

13. $\frac{51}{20}$
14. $\frac{43}{10}$
15. $\frac{31}{6}$
16. $\frac{53}{24}$

REWRITING A FRACTION
IN SIMPLEST TERMS

----

48. **If any number is multiplied by 1, what number do we obtain?**

The number we started with; multiplying any number by 1 leaves the number unchanged.

----

49. Show this in some examples.

$$1 \times 2 = 2$$
$$1 \times 3 = 3$$
$$1 \times \tfrac{2}{3} = \tfrac{2}{3}$$

---

50. What name in modern mathematics is given to this multiplicative property of 1?

The identity property.

---

51. In modern mathematics, what name is given to a number that when used as a multiplier leaves unchanged the number multiplied?

The identity element for multiplication.

---

52. What number is the identity element for multiplication?

1 (and all the fraction names for 1, such as $\tfrac{2}{2}$, $\tfrac{3}{3}$, $\tfrac{4}{4}$, $\tfrac{5}{5}$, $\tfrac{10}{10}$, and $\tfrac{100}{100}$)

---

53. Why is the identity element for multiplication important?

Because (as the frames immediately following will show) use of the identity element makes it possible to rewrite fractions as equivalent expressions having other denominators. (NOTE: As we will see in Frames 116–136, addition and subtraction of fractions is possible only when the fractions have the same denominator.)

---

54. Why is 1 the identity element for multiplication?

Because if any number is multiplied (or divided) by 1 (or any of the fraction names for 1, such as $\frac{2}{2}$, $\frac{4}{4}$, $\frac{8}{8}$, $\frac{10}{10}$, and $\frac{40}{40}$), the number itself is unchanged.

---

55. How do we know that $\frac{5}{10}$ is the same number as $\frac{1}{2}$?

Because $\frac{1}{2} \times \frac{5}{5}$ (which is just another name for 1) $= \frac{1 \times 5}{2 \times 5} = \frac{5}{10}$. Similarly, $\frac{5}{10} \div \frac{5}{5} = \frac{5 \div 5}{10 \div 5} = \frac{1}{2}$.

---

56. Does $\frac{10}{20}$ have the same value (that is, name the same number) as $\frac{1}{2}$?

Yes, for the same reason that $\frac{5}{10} = \frac{1}{2}$.

---

57. Does the expression $\frac{40}{80}$ name the same number (that is, have the same value) as $\frac{1}{2}$, $\frac{5}{10}$, and $\frac{10}{20}$?

Yes, because $\frac{40 \div 40}{80 \div 40} = \frac{1}{2}$; $\frac{40 \div 8}{80 \div 8} = \frac{5}{10}$; and $\frac{40 \div 4}{80 \div 4} = \frac{10}{20}$.

---

58. What fact is illustrated by the preceding examples?

That if both the numerator and denominator of a fraction are multiplied (or divided) by the same number, the value of the fraction remains the same. This is just another way of saying that if any number is multiplied (or divided) by the identity element (1, or any fraction name for 1), the number itself is unchanged.

59. What especially is to be noted about the relation of $\frac{10}{20}$ and $\frac{5}{10}$?

That although both have the same value, $\frac{5}{10}$ has lower terms than $\frac{10}{20}$.

60. What number is an exact divisor of both 5 and 10?

5.

61. If we divide both the 5 and 10 of $\frac{5}{10}$ by five $\left(\text{that is, } \dfrac{5 \div 5}{10 \div 5}\right)$ we reduce the expression to $\frac{1}{2}$. But can both the numerator and the denominator of $\frac{1}{2}$ be divided exactly by any number greater than 1?

No.

62. What, then, can we say specifically about the relation of $\frac{1}{2}$ to its equivalent expressions $\frac{5}{10}$, $\frac{10}{20}$, etc.?

That $\frac{1}{2}$ expresses the given fraction in its simplest form (lowest terms).

---

63. What do we call a number that is an exact divisor of two (or more) numbers?

A common divisor of these numbers.

---

64. What is a greatest common divisor?

The largest number that is an exact divisor of the given numbers.

---

65. Give some examples of greatest common divisors.

3 is the greatest common divisor of 6 and 9.

4 is the greatest common divisor of 8, 12, and 16.

5 is the greatest common divisor of 10, 15, 25, and 40.

---

66. How can any fraction be reduced to its simplest form?

By dividing its numerator and denominator by the largest number that is an exact divisor of both; that is, by their greatest common divisor.

---

67. Show this in an example.

Reduce $\frac{12}{16}$ to its simplest form.

4 is the greatest common divisor of both 12 and 16.

$$\frac{12 \div 4}{16 \div 4} = \frac{3}{4}$$

---

68. Reduce $\frac{20}{25}$ to its simplest form.

5 is the greatest common divisor (largest exact divisor) of both 20 and 25.

$$\frac{20 \div 5}{25 \div 5} = \frac{4}{5}$$

---

69. Reduce $\frac{40}{120}$ to its simplest form.

40 is the greatest common divisor (largest exact divisor) of both 40 and 120.

$$\frac{40 \div 40}{120 \div 40} = \frac{1}{3}$$

---

1. If any number is multiplied by 1, the number itself is not _____.

_____ [48]

2. $1 \times \frac{3}{4} =$ _____.

_____ [49]

3. The property of 1 that enables it, when used as a multiplier, to leave the number multiplied _____ is called the _____ property.

_____ [50]

4. The number that when used as a multiplier leaves unchanged the number multiplied is called the _____ _____ for multiplication.

_____ [51]

5. The number which is the _____ _____ for multiplication is _____.

_____ [52]

6. It is important in operations with fractions to be able to rewrite any fraction as an equivalent expression having another _____.

_____ [53]

7. $\frac{2}{2}$, $\frac{4}{4}$, $\frac{8}{8}$, $\frac{10}{10}$, are different fraction names for the _____ element, or the integer (whole number) _____.

_____ [54]

8. $\frac{1 \times ?}{2 \times ?} = \frac{5}{10}$. _____

_____[55]

9. $\frac{10}{20}$ and $\frac{1}{2}$ name the same _____.

_____[56]

10. Use of the identity principle for multiplication illustrates the fact that if both the numerator and the denominator of a fraction are multiplied by the same number, the value of the fraction is _____.

_____[58]

11. Although $\frac{5}{10}$ and $\frac{10}{20}$ both name the same number, $\frac{5}{10}$ expresses that number in _____ terms.

_____[59]

12. 5 is an exact _____ of both 5 and 10.

_____[60]

13. There is no whole number greater than _____ that is an exact divisor of both 1 and 2.

_____[61]

14. $\frac{1}{2}$ names the _____ form of the number whose other fraction names are $\frac{5}{10}$, $\frac{10}{20}$, etc.

_____[62]

15. A common divisor of two (or more) numbers is a number that is an _____ divisor of both (or all).

_____[63]

16. The greatest common divisor of two or more numbers is the _____ number that is an _____ divisor of the given numbers.

_____[64]

17. The greatest common divisor of 8, 12, and 16 is

_____.

_____[65]

18. To rewrite any fraction in its simplest form, all we have to do is divide both the numerator and the denominator by their _____ _____ divisor.

_____[66]

19. The simplest form of $\frac{12}{16}$ is found by dividing both 12 and 16 by what number? _____

_____[67]

20. $\frac{40 \div ?}{120 \div ?} = \frac{1}{3}$. _____

_____[69]

Practice Exercise 3: Rewriting Fractions

Reduce the following fractions to simplest forms (lowest terms):

1. $\frac{18}{48}$ 4. $\frac{12}{60}$
2. $\frac{15}{20}$ 5. $\frac{18}{24}$
3. $\frac{35}{56}$ 6. $\frac{9}{144}$

Reduce the following fractions to whole numbers or mixed forms:

7. $\frac{10}{5}$ 11. $\frac{33}{9}$
8. $\frac{31}{20}$ 12. $\frac{36}{4}$
9. $\frac{65}{20}$ 13. $\frac{26}{3}$
10. $\frac{45}{8}$ 14. $\frac{100}{10}$

1. Changed
2. $\frac{3}{4}$
3. Unchanged; identity
4. Identity element
5. Identity element; 1
6. Denominator
7. Identity; 1
8. $\frac{5}{5}$
9. Number
10. Unchanged
11. Lower
12. Divisor
13. 1
14. Simplest
15. Exact
16. Largest (or greatest); exact
17. 4
18. Greatest common
19. 4
20. 40

ANSWERS: PRACTICE EXERCISE 3

1. $\frac{3}{8}$
2. $\frac{3}{4}$
3. $\frac{5}{8}$
4. $\frac{1}{5}$
5. $\frac{3}{4}$
6. $\frac{1}{16}$

7. 2
8. $1\frac{11}{20}$
9. $3\frac{1}{4}$
10. $5\frac{5}{8}$
11. $3\frac{2}{3}$
12. 9
13. $8\frac{2}{3}$
14. 10

MULTIPLYING FRACTIONS

70. If 2 times $\frac{1}{3}$ is $\frac{2}{3}$, what is 3 times $\frac{1}{4}$?

$$\frac{3 \times 1}{4} = \frac{3}{4}.$$

71. What is 5 times $\frac{1}{15}$?

$$\frac{5 \times 1}{15} = \frac{5}{15}.$$

72. What conclusion can we draw from these examples?

That to multiply a fraction by a whole number (integer), all we do is multiply the numerator by the whole number. We leave the denominator unchanged (that is, the product is placed over the original denominator).

73. Now apply this rule in an example not quite so simple. What is $7 \times \frac{2}{3}$?

$$\frac{7 \times 2}{3} = \frac{14}{3}.$$

74. What kind of a fraction is $\frac{14}{3}$?

An improper fraction (that is, a fraction whose value is greater than 1).

75. Can we express $\frac{14}{3}$ as a mixed form?

Easily. All we do is perform the indicated division.

---

76. What is the mixed form whose value is $\frac{14}{3}$?

$$4\frac{2}{3} \quad Ans.$$
$$3\,)\overline{14}$$

---

77. Does an improper fraction always represent a mixed form?

No. An improper fraction often has the same value as a whole number.

---

78. Give an example of multiplication of a fraction by a whole number in which the product can be expressed as a whole number.

$6 \times \frac{2}{3}$. The product is $\frac{12}{3}$, or 4.

---

79. In both of the examples considered above, what final operation did we perform?

We reduced the answer (fraction) to its simplest form. (Note that $4 = \frac{4}{1}$, a fraction that has no exact divisor greater than 1.)

---

80. Multiply $\frac{1}{2} \times \frac{1}{2}$.

$$\frac{1}{2} \times \frac{1}{2} = \frac{1 \times 1}{2 \times 2} = \frac{1}{4}.$$

---

81. Multiply $\frac{1}{4} \times \frac{1}{4}$.

$$\frac{1}{4} \times \frac{1}{4} = \frac{1 \times 1}{4 \times 4} = \frac{1}{16}.$$

82. Now multiply $\frac{3}{4} \times \frac{3}{4}$.

$$\frac{3}{4} \times \frac{3}{4} = \frac{3 \times 3}{4 \times 4} = \frac{9}{16}.$$

83. From these three examples, what rule can we derive for multiplying one fraction by another?

RULE: To multiply one fraction by another, we multiply the numerators together (to obtain a new numerator) and multiply the denominators together (to obtain a new denominator).

84. If several fractions are to be multiplied together, do we proceed in the same way?

Yes. Finding the product of three or more fractions is just a continuation of the operation used to find the product of two fractions.

85. Show this in an example.

Find the product of $\frac{2}{3} \times \frac{3}{5} \times \frac{4}{7}$.

$$\frac{2 \times 3 \times 4}{3 \times 5 \times 7} = \frac{24}{105}.$$

86. **Is it necessary to reduce a fraction like $\frac{24}{105}$ to its lowest terms?**

> No, but it is sometimes more convenient to work with fractions in their lowest terms. Thus, since both 24 and 105 can be divided exactly by 3, $\frac{24}{105}$ can be reduced to $\frac{8}{35}$.

1. $\frac{3}{4} = 3 \times \frac{?}{?}$. _____

   _____[70]

2. $\frac{5}{15} = ? \times \frac{1}{15}$. _____

   _____[71]

3. To multiply a fraction by a whole number, we first multiply the _____ of the fraction by the whole number, then write this product over the original _____.

   _____[72]

4. Is $\frac{14}{3}$ a proper or improper fraction? _____

   _____[74]

5. If we perform the indicated division of $\frac{14}{3}$, the result (quotient) is a _____ form.

   _____[75]

6. Express $4\frac{2}{3}$ as an improper fraction. _____

   _____[76]

7. An improper fraction can be expressed as a(n) _____ form, unless it happens to represent a whole number.

   _____[77]

8. If we reduced $\frac{25}{5}$ to its simplest form, the answer would be a _____ number.

   _____[78]

9. When a fraction has been reduced to its simplest form, it has no exact divisor greater than _____.

_____[79]

10. To multiply one fraction by another, we multiply the _____ together and the _____ together.

_____[83]

11. Finding the product of three or more fractions is merely a continuation of the operation used to find the _____ of _____ fractions.

_____[84]

12. It is usually more convenient to work with fractions (such as $\frac{25}{105}$) when they are expressed in their _____ form.

_____[86]

Practice Exercise 4: Multiplying One Fraction by Another

Find the following products:

1. $\frac{1}{2} \times \frac{1}{5}$
2. $\frac{2}{3} \times \frac{3}{5}$
3. $\frac{5}{7} \times \frac{5}{8}$
4. $\frac{11}{12} \times \frac{2}{5}$
5. $\frac{20}{7} \times \frac{3}{8}$
6. $\frac{1}{3} \times \frac{1}{5} \times \frac{3}{5}$

7. $\frac{5}{6} \times \frac{1}{2} \times \frac{2}{9}$
8. $\frac{6}{5} \times \frac{2}{3} \times \frac{7}{11}$
9. $\frac{8}{9} \times \frac{5}{11} \times \frac{9}{12}$
10. $\frac{3}{5} \times \frac{2}{9} \times \frac{17}{123}$
11. $\frac{2}{3} \times \frac{4}{9} \times \frac{1}{2} \times \frac{7}{10}$
12. $\frac{1}{2} \times \frac{6}{5} \times \frac{8}{9} \times \frac{15}{14}$

DIVISION OF FRACTIONS

87. If we turn a fraction upside down (that is, interchange the numerator and denominator), what do we call the expression that results?

The reciprocal (or inverse) of the original fraction.

88. What is $\frac{4}{3}$ in relation to $\frac{3}{4}$?

$\frac{4}{3}$ is the reciprocal (inverse) of $\frac{3}{4}$.

89. What is the reciprocal of $\frac{1}{2}$?

$\frac{2}{1}$ (that is, 2).

90. Multiply $\frac{3}{4}$ by its reciprocal.

$\frac{3}{4} \times \frac{4}{3} = \frac{12}{12} = 1$.

91. Multiply $\frac{1}{2}$ by its reciprocal.

$\frac{1}{2} \times \frac{2}{1} = \frac{2}{2} = 1$.

92. What do these two examples tell us about the property of reciprocals?

If any number is multiplied by its reciprocal, the product is 1.

1. $\frac{1}{4}$
2. 5
3. Numerator; denominator
4. Improper
5. Mixed
6. $\frac{14}{3}$

7. Mixed
8. Whole
9. 1
10. Numerators; denominators
11. Product; two
12. Simplest

ANSWERS: PRACTICE EXERCISE 4

1. $\frac{1}{10}$
2. $\frac{6}{15}$ (or $\frac{2}{5}$)
3. $\frac{25}{56}$
4. $\frac{22}{60}$ (or $\frac{11}{30}$)
5. $\frac{60}{56}$ (or $1\frac{1}{14}$)
6. $\frac{3}{75}$ (or $\frac{1}{25}$)

7. $\frac{10}{108}$ (or $\frac{5}{54}$)
8. $\frac{84}{165}$ (or $\frac{28}{55}$)
9. $\frac{360}{1188}$ (or $\frac{10}{33}$)
10. $\frac{102}{5535}$ (or $\frac{34}{1845}$)
11. $\frac{56}{540}$ (or $\frac{14}{135}$)
12. $\frac{720}{1260}$ (or $\frac{4}{7}$)

---

93. Does every number that can be expressed in fractional form have a reciprocal?

Every rational number (except 0) has a reciprocal. (NOTE: A rational number is a number that can be expressed in the form $\frac{a}{b}$, where a and b are integers, and b is not 0. Examples: 1, 2, 3, $\frac{1}{2}$, $\frac{2}{5}$, $\frac{3}{4}$, etc.)

---

94. What is the easiest way to divide a whole number by a fraction (a number in fractional form)?

Invert the fraction, then multiply (that is, multiply the whole number by the reciprocal of the fraction).

---

95. Show this in an illustration.

Divide 4 by $\frac{1}{2}$.
$$4 \div \frac{1}{2} = 4 \times \frac{2}{1} = 8$$

---

6. Does the same principle apply to dividing one fraction by another?

Yes. Simply invert the fraction that is the divisor (the fraction by which the other is to be divided), then multiply.

7. Divide $\frac{2}{3}$ by $\frac{1}{2}$.

$$\frac{2}{3} \div \frac{1}{2} = \frac{2}{3} \times \frac{2}{1} = \frac{4}{3}.$$

8. Divide $\frac{2}{3}$ by $\frac{3}{4}$.

$$\frac{2}{3} \div \frac{3}{4} = \frac{2}{3} \times \frac{4}{3} = \frac{8}{9}.$$

9. In general, would we follow the same procedure if we wanted to divide a fraction by a whole number?

Yes. We would simply write the whole number with 1 as a denominator, then invert this expression and multiply.

100. Divide $\frac{1}{2}$ by 4.

$$\frac{1}{2} \div 4 = \frac{1}{2} \div \frac{4}{1} = \frac{1}{2} \times \frac{1}{4} = \frac{1}{8}.$$

101. In terms of modern mathematics, what do we do when we divide one number by another?

We perform an operation equivalent to multiplying by the reciprocal of the divisor.

102. Show this in an example using whole numbers

$$4 \div 2 = 4 \times \tfrac{1}{2} = 2.$$

103. In modern mathematics, is there a special name for the reciprocal of a number, when this reciprocal is applied to the operation of multiplication?

Yes. A reciprocal, in this sense, is called the multiplicative inverse.

104. Define the multiplicative inverse of a number.

The number which when used as a multiplier of the given number (except 0) produces 1 as a product.

105. Now, combining these definitions, state a formal rule for dividing any number by a fraction.

Multiply the number to be divided by the multiplicative inverse of the fraction.

106. What does this mean in plain English?

To divide a number by a fraction, invert the the fraction and multiply. (NOTE: It is always the divisor that is inverted, never the number that is to be divided.)

07. Now divide $2\frac{1}{2}$ by 3.

The problem is no more difficult than the ones we have already considered. Express $2\frac{1}{2}$ as an improper fraction, then proceed as before.

$$2\frac{1}{2} \div 3 = \frac{5}{2} \div 3 = \frac{5}{2} \div \frac{3}{1} = \frac{5}{2} \times \frac{1}{3}$$
$$= \frac{5 \times 1}{2 \times 3} = \frac{5}{6}$$

08. Divide 3 by $2\frac{1}{2}$.

Again:

$$3 \div 2\frac{1}{2} = 3 \div \frac{5}{2} = \frac{3}{1} \times \frac{2}{5}$$
$$= \frac{3 \times 2}{1 \times 5} = \frac{6}{5} \quad (\text{or } 1\frac{1}{5})$$

1. We can obtain the reciprocal of a fraction by inter
   changing the positions of the _____ and _____

   _____ [87]

2. In ordinary language, it could be said that to obtain
   the reciprocal of a fraction all we have to do is turn
   the fraction _____.

   _____ [87]

3. The reciprocal of $\frac{4}{3}$ is _____.

   _____ [88]

4. $\frac{4}{5} \times \frac{5}{4} =$ _____.

   _____ [90]

5. $\frac{2}{1} \times \frac{?}{?} = 1.$ _____

   _____ [91]

6. If any number is multiplied by its reciprocal, the
   product is _____.

   _____ [92]

7. Every _____ number (except 0) has a reciprocal.

   _____ [93]

8. The easiest way to divide a whole number by a fraction is to invert the fraction, then _____.

   _____ [94]

54

9. $5 \div \frac{1}{3} = 5 \times \frac{?}{?} = 15.$ _____

_____[95]

0. To divide one fraction by another fraction, we simply invert (take the reciprocal of) the fraction that is the

_____, then _____.

_____[96]

1. $\frac{2}{5} \div \frac{3}{4} = \frac{?}{?} \times \frac{?}{?} = \frac{8}{15}.$ _____

_____[97]

2. If we want to divide a fraction by a whole number (integer), we write the whole number in fraction form,

with _____ as a denominator, then invert this expression and _____.

_____[99]

3. $\frac{1}{3} \div 5 = \frac{1}{3} \div \frac{?}{?} = \frac{1}{3} \times \frac{?}{?} = \frac{1}{15}.$ _____

_____[100]

4. To divide any number by another is equivalent to multiplying the first number (number to be divided)

by the _____ of the other (divisor).

_____[101]

5. In modern mathematics, the term *multiplicative inverse* of a number refers to the _____ of that number.

_____[103]

6. The multiplicative inverse of a number can be defined as a number that when used as a multiplier of the given

number (except 0) results in _____ as a product.

_____[104]

17. Using the terminology of the new mathematics, we can say that to divide a number by another is equivalent to multiplying the first number (number to be divided) by the _____ _____ of the other.

_____ [105]

18. In the division of fractions, it is important to remember that it is always the _____ that is inverted never the _____ _____ _____.

_____ [106]

19. If one of the numbers in a division problem is in mixed form (EXAMPLE: $2\frac{3}{4}$), it is usually helpful to rewrite the mixed form as a(n) _____ fraction.

_____ [107–108]

Practice Exercise 5: Division of Fractions

Perform the following divisions and reduce answer to lowest terms:

1. $\frac{3}{8} \div \frac{2}{3}$ 9. $\frac{2}{9} \div \frac{1}{2}$

2. $2\frac{1}{3} \div 1\frac{1}{2}$ 10. $3\frac{3}{4} \div \frac{5}{8}$

3. $\frac{5}{8} \div \frac{5}{16}$ 11. $\frac{3}{20} \div 5$

4. $\frac{1}{3} \div \frac{4}{6}$ 12. $4\frac{2}{3} \div 2\frac{4}{5}$

5. $\frac{3}{10} \div \frac{3}{4}$ 13. $2\frac{1}{6} \div 2\frac{2}{3}$

6. $\frac{7}{28}\frac{2}{}$ 14. $8 \div \frac{4}{9}$

7. $\frac{3}{4} \div \frac{3}{20}$ 15. $\frac{4}{9} \div \frac{1}{6}$

8. $14 \div \frac{7}{10}$

CANCELLATION

109. Is there a short cut in multiplying (or dividing) two or more large fractions?

Yes. By cancellation.

110. What is cancellation?

The operation of reducing both numerator and denominator of a fraction by removing a factor common to both. EXAMPLE:

$$\tfrac{3}{2} \times 4 = \frac{3 \times 4}{2} = \tfrac{12}{2} = 6$$

But if we divide the factor 2 into both numerator and denominator we would have

$$\frac{3 \times \overset{2}{\cancel{4}}}{\underset{1}{\cancel{2}}} = \frac{3 \times 2}{1} = 6$$

111. What is the principle behind cancellation?

We have already learned (Frames 48–58) that if terms in both the numerator and denominator of a fraction are divided (or multiplied) by the same number, the value of the fraction is unchanged (in short, multiplying or dividing a number by the identity element for multiplication, 1, leaves the number unchanged).

1. Numerator; denominator
2. Upside down
3. $\frac{3}{4}$
4. 1
5. $\frac{1}{2}$
6. 1
7. Rational
8. Multiply
9. $\frac{3}{1}$
10. Divisor; multiply
11. $\frac{2}{5}$; $\frac{4}{3}$
12. 1; multiply
13. $\frac{5}{1}$; $\frac{1}{5}$
14. Reciprocal
15. Reciprocal
16. 1
17. Multiplicative inverse
18. Divisor; number to divided (or dividend)
19. Improper

ANSWERS: PRACTICE EXERCISE 5

1. $\frac{9}{16}$
2. $1\frac{5}{9}$
3. 2
4. $\frac{1}{2}$
5. $\frac{2}{5}$
6. $2\frac{4}{7}$
7. 5
8. 20
9. $\frac{4}{9}$
10. 6
11. $\frac{3}{100}$
12. $1\frac{2}{3}$
13. $1\frac{3}{16}$
14. 18
15. $2\frac{2}{3}$

112. Does cancellation actually simplify multiplication of fractions?

It often does. Consider the following example:
$$\tfrac{1}{3} \times \tfrac{3}{2} \times \tfrac{2}{5}$$

By the long method, we have
$$\frac{1 \times 3 \times 2}{3 \times 2 \times 5} = \tfrac{6}{30} = \tfrac{1}{5}$$

But if we cancel out 3s and 2s (common to both numerator and denominator), we have
$$\frac{1 \times \cancel{3} \times \cancel{2}}{\cancel{3} \times \cancel{2} \times 5} = \tfrac{1}{5}$$

113. Using cancellation, find the product $\frac{2}{3} \times \frac{6}{4} \times \frac{5}{9}$

$$\frac{\overset{1}{\underset{1}{2}} \times \overset{\overset{1}{2}}{\underset{2}{6}} \times 5}{\underset{1}{3} \times \underset{2}{4} \times \underset{1}{9}} = \frac{5}{9}.$$

(In this case we have applied the cancellation operation a second time—to reduce the fraction further.)

---

114. Can cancellation be used to simplify multiplication of mixed forms?

Often, yes. But the mixed forms must first be expressed as improper fractions.

---

115. Show this in an example.

Find the product of $2\frac{1}{4} \times 3\frac{1}{3}$.

$$2\frac{1}{4} \times 3\frac{1}{3} = \frac{\overset{3}{9} \times \overset{5}{10}}{\underset{2}{4} \times \underset{1}{3}} = \frac{15}{2} = 7\frac{1}{2}.$$

---

1. Cancellation is an operation that simplifies _____ or _____ of two or more large fractions.

_____[109]

2. Cancellation consists of removing from both the numerator and denominator of a fraction (or fractions) a factor that is _____ to both.

_____[110]

3. In the expression $\frac{3 \times 4}{4}$, the common factor is _____ .

_____[110]

4. Cancellation is justified by the fact that if a fraction is multiplied (or divided) by 1, the value of the fraction is _____ .

_____[111]

5. In the expression $\frac{1 \times 3 \times 2}{3 \times 2 \times 5}$, we can cancel out the _____ and _____ .

_____[112]

6. Cancellation can often be used in multiplying mixed numbers if the mixed numbers are first expressed as _____ .

_____[114]

1. Multiplication; division
2. Common
3. 4
4. Unchanged
5. 3s; 2s
6. Improper fractions

Practice Exercise 6: Cancellation

Find the following products, canceling wherever possible:

1. $\frac{5}{8} \times 12$
2. $5 \times \frac{4}{9}$
3. $\frac{1}{3} \times \frac{2}{3}$
4. $\frac{1}{2} \times \frac{1}{3} \times \frac{2}{5}$
5. $\frac{3}{4} \times 6$
6. $\frac{4}{3} \times \frac{1}{6}$
7. $6 \times \frac{2}{3}$

8. $10\frac{1}{2} \times 3\frac{1}{3}$
9. $1\frac{5}{6} \times 13$
10. $8\frac{3}{4} \times \frac{2}{5}$
11. $\frac{7}{12} \times \frac{3}{5}$
12. $\frac{2}{5} \times \frac{1}{2}$
13. $\frac{8}{2} \times \frac{6}{3} \times \frac{12}{4}$

1. $7\frac{1}{2}$
2. $2\frac{2}{9}$
3. $\frac{2}{9}$
4. $\frac{1}{15}$
5. $4\frac{1}{2}$
6. $\frac{2}{9}$
7. 4

8. 35
9. $23\frac{5}{6}$
10. $3\frac{1}{2}$
11. $\frac{7}{20}$
12. $\frac{1}{5}$
13. 24

ADDITION AND SUBTRACTION OF FRACTIONS

---

116. If $\frac{1}{3} + \frac{1}{3} = \frac{2}{3}$, what is $\frac{1}{4} + \frac{2}{4}$?

$\frac{3}{4}$.

---

117. What is $\frac{4}{9} + \frac{3}{9}$?

$\frac{7}{9}$.

---

118. What fact is illustrated in the above examples?

That to add two fractions that have the same denominator, we merely add the numerators and leave the denominator unchanged.

---

119. Can we add $\frac{1}{2}$ and $\frac{1}{3}$?

Yes, providing we express both fractions as fractions that have the same denominator (that is, a common denominator).

120. What is the common denominator of two or more fractions?

The same denominator. If, say, $\frac{1}{2}$ and $\frac{3}{4}$ are expressed as $\frac{2}{4}$ and $\frac{3}{4}$, both fractions are named in terms of 4ths; the denominator then common to both expressions is 4.

121. How can we find a denominator common to two or more fractions?

One way is to multiply the denominators together. EXAMPLE: To find a common denominator of $\frac{1}{2}$, $\frac{1}{3}$, and $\frac{1}{4}$, multiply $2 \times 3 \times 4$. The product is 24. This is not the smallest denominator common to all of these fractions, but it is one common denominator. (The smallest denominator common to $\frac{1}{2}$, $\frac{1}{3}$, and $\frac{1}{4}$ is 12.)

122. What name is usually given to the smallest denominator common to two or more fractional expressions?

Least common denominator.

123. **What is another way of defining the least (lowest) common denominator of two or more fractions?**

The least common multiple of the denominators. NOTE: To find the least common multiple of two or more numbers, divide all the factorable numbers by their prime divisors (divisors which themselves have no exact divisors; EXAMPLES: 2, 3, 5); repeat with the quotient, bringing down any number not yet factored; continue until all factors have been found, then multiply together the final quotients and these divisors. Thus, to find the least common multiple of 2, 6, and 15:

$$\begin{array}{r} 2/\overline{2,\ 6,\ 15} \\ 3/\overline{1,\ 3,\ 15} \\ \overline{1,\ 1,\ \ 5} \end{array}$$

Least common multiple
$$= 2 \times 3 \times 1 \times 1 \times 5 = 30$$

124. **Express $\frac{1}{2}$ and $\frac{1}{3}$ as fractions with a common denominator.**

$\frac{1}{2} = \frac{3}{6}$
$\frac{1}{3} = \frac{2}{6}$

125. **Now add $\frac{1}{2}$ and $\frac{1}{3}$.**

$$\frac{1}{2} + \frac{1}{3} = \frac{3}{6} + \frac{2}{6} = \frac{3+2}{6} = \frac{5}{6}.$$

126. **Add $\frac{2}{3}$ and $\frac{3}{4}$.**

$$\frac{2}{3} + \frac{3}{4} = \frac{8}{12} + \frac{9}{12} = \frac{17}{12} \quad \text{(or } 1\frac{5}{12}\text{)}.$$

127. **What is a common denominator of $\frac{1}{2}$, $\frac{1}{5}$, $\frac{1}{8}$?**

$2 \times 5 \times 8 = 80.$

128. **What is the least common denominator of $\frac{1}{2}$, $\frac{1}{5}$, $\frac{1}{8}$?**

40.

129. **In adding or subtracting fractions does it make any difference whether the fractions are expressed as equivalent fractions in terms of the least common denominator or in terms of any common denominator?**

No. It is sometimes more convenient, however, to work with the least common denominator, if this can be found without extensive calculation.

130. **From the foregoing examples, derive a rule for finding a common denominator of two or more fractions.**

RULE: Multiply the denominators together. (NOTE: It is not necessary to use any factor more than once. Thus the common denominator of $\frac{1}{4}$, $\frac{3}{4}$, $\frac{2}{5}$, and $\frac{4}{5}$ is simply 4×5, or 20.)

131. **Can we subtract $\frac{2}{4}$ from $\frac{3}{4}$?**

Yes. Both fractions are alike (that is, have the same denominator). So we leave the denominator unchanged and simply subtract one numerator from the other. Thus

$$\frac{3}{4} - \frac{2}{4} = \frac{1}{4}.$$

132. Subtract $\frac{4}{9}$ from $\frac{6}{9}$.

$$\frac{6}{9} - \frac{4}{9} = \frac{2}{9}.$$

133. Can we subtract one fraction from another if the two fractions are unlike (that is, have different denominators)?

Yes. But we must first rewrite the given fractions as fractions having a common denominator (but equivalent in value to the given expressions).

134. Now subtract $\frac{2}{3}$ from $\frac{3}{4}$.

$$\frac{3}{4} - \frac{2}{3} = \frac{9}{12} - \frac{8}{12} = \frac{1}{12}.$$

135. Subtract $\frac{3}{4}$ from $\frac{4}{5}$.

$$\frac{4}{5} - \frac{3}{4} = \frac{16}{20} - \frac{15}{20} = \frac{1}{20}.$$

136. From the preceding two examples, state a general rule for the subtraction of unlike fractions.

RULE: Express both fractions as fractions having a common denominator; then subtract one numerator from the other (as indicated) as you would subtract one integer from another. The difference is written over the common denominator.

1. $\frac{3}{4} + \frac{2}{4} =$ _____.

   _____[116]

2. To add two fractions that have the same denominator,

   we add the _____, but leave the _____ unchanged.

   _____[118]

3. We can add fractions that have unlike denominators

   if, first, we express both in terms of the _____
   denominator.

   _____[119]

4. $\frac{1}{2}$ and $\frac{1}{3}$ have _____ as a _____ denominator.

   _____[120]

5. 15 is a _____ denominator of $\frac{2}{3}$ and $\frac{3}{?}$. _____

   _____[120]

6. Two or more fractions have a number of denominators
   in common, but it is usually most convenient to work

   with the _____.

   _____[122]

7. To find a _____ denominator of two or more frac-

   tions, it is only necessary to _____ the denominators together.

   _____[121, 130]

8. $\frac{1}{4} = \frac{3}{4} - \frac{?}{4}$. _____

_____[131]

9. $\frac{5}{7} - \frac{3}{7} =$ _____.

_____[131]

10. To subtract one fraction from another if the fractions are unlike (that is, have different denominators), it is first necessary to rewrite the fractions as equivalent

expressions having _____ denominator.

_____[136]

Practice Exercise 7: Addition and Subtraction of Fractions

Add:

1. $\frac{2}{7} + \frac{3}{7}$
2. $\frac{1}{3} + \frac{2}{5}$
3. $\frac{2}{5} + \frac{2}{7}$
4. $\frac{3}{7} + \frac{4}{9}$
5. $\frac{3}{8} + \frac{19}{3}$
6. $\frac{3}{8} + 6\frac{1}{3}$
7. $\frac{1}{2} + \frac{1}{3} + \frac{1}{5}$
8. $\frac{1}{2} + \frac{2}{3} + \frac{3}{5}$
9. $\frac{1}{2} + \frac{2}{3} + \frac{3}{4} + \frac{1}{5}$
10. $2\frac{1}{3} + 3\frac{1}{2}$

Subtract:

11. $\frac{3}{7} - \frac{2}{7}$
12. $\frac{2}{5} - \frac{1}{3}$
13. $\frac{2}{5} - \frac{2}{7}$
14. $\frac{4}{9} - \frac{3}{7}$
15. $\frac{19}{3} - \frac{3}{8}$
16. $6\frac{1}{3} - \frac{3}{8}$
17. $3\frac{1}{2} - 2\frac{1}{3}$

1. $\frac{5}{4}$ (or $1\frac{1}{4}$)
2. Numerators; denominator
3. Same
4. 6; Common (Note that 6 is the smallest, but not the only common denominator of $\frac{1}{2}$ and $\frac{1}{3}$.)
5. Common; 5 ($\frac{3}{5}$)
6. Smallest
7. Common; multiply
8. 2 ($\frac{2}{4}$)
9. $\frac{2}{7}$
10. A common (or, the same)

ANSWERS: PRACTICE EXERCISE 7

(NOTE: Because some of problems in this exercise may introduce special difficulties, the answers detail the successive steps in each operation.)

1. $\frac{2}{7} + \frac{3}{7} = \frac{5}{7}$

2. $\frac{1}{3} + \frac{2}{5} = \frac{5}{15} + \frac{6}{15} = \frac{11}{15}$

3. $\frac{2}{5} + \frac{2}{7} = \frac{14}{35} + \frac{10}{35} = \frac{24}{35}$

4. $\frac{3}{7} + \frac{4}{9} = \frac{27}{63} + \frac{28}{63} = \frac{55}{63}$

5. $\frac{3}{8} + \frac{19}{3} = \frac{9}{24} + \frac{152}{24}$
   $= \frac{161}{24} = 6\frac{17}{24}$

6. $\frac{3}{8} + 6\frac{1}{3} = \frac{3}{8} + \frac{19}{3}$
   $= \frac{9}{24} + \frac{152}{24} = \frac{161}{24} = 6\frac{17}{24}$

7. $\frac{1}{2} + \frac{1}{3} + \frac{1}{5} = \frac{15}{30} + \frac{10}{30} + \frac{6}{30}$
   $= \frac{31}{30} = 1\frac{1}{30}$

8. $\frac{1}{2} + \frac{2}{3} + \frac{3}{5} = \frac{15}{30} + \frac{20}{30} + \frac{18}{30}$
   $= \frac{53}{30} = 1\frac{23}{30}$

9. $\frac{1}{2} + \frac{2}{3} + \frac{3}{4} + \frac{1}{5}$
   $= \frac{30}{60} + \frac{40}{60} + \frac{45}{60} + \frac{12}{60}$
   $= \frac{127}{60} = 2\frac{7}{60}$

10. $2\frac{1}{3} + 3\frac{1}{2} = \frac{7}{3} + \frac{7}{2}$
    $= \frac{14}{6} + \frac{21}{6} = \frac{35}{6} = 5\frac{5}{6}$

11. $\frac{3}{7} - \frac{2}{7} = \frac{1}{7}$

12. $\frac{2}{5} - \frac{1}{3} = \frac{6}{15} - \frac{5}{15} = \frac{1}{15}$

13. $\frac{2}{5} - \frac{2}{7} = \frac{14}{35} - \frac{10}{35} = \frac{4}{35}$

14. $\frac{4}{9} - \frac{3}{7} = \frac{28}{63} - \frac{27}{63} = \frac{1}{63}$

15. $\frac{19}{3} - \frac{3}{8} = \frac{152}{24} - \frac{9}{24}$
    $= \frac{143}{24} = 5\frac{23}{24}$

16. $6\frac{1}{3} - \frac{3}{8} = \frac{19}{3} - \frac{3}{8}$
    $= \frac{152}{24} - \frac{9}{24} = \frac{143}{24}$
    $= 5\frac{23}{24}$

17. $3\frac{1}{2} - 2\frac{1}{3} = \frac{7}{2} - \frac{7}{3}$
    $= \frac{21}{6} - \frac{14}{6} = \frac{7}{6} = 1\frac{1}{6}$

DECIMALS

READING AND WRITING
DECIMAL FRACTIONS

---

137. What is the difference between 0.1 and $\frac{1}{10}$?

There is no difference in value. 0.1 is simply another way of writing $\frac{1}{10}$.

---

138. What is the difference between 0.01 and $\frac{1}{100}$?

There is no essential difference. 0.01 has the same meaning as $\frac{1}{100}$.

---

139. What name do we usually give to fractions of the form 0.1, 0.02, 0.003, 0.0005, etc.?

Decimal fractions, or simply *decimals*.

---

140. What name is given to decimal expressions (such as 2.3 or 4.6) that consist of a whole number and a decimal fraction?

Decimal mixed fractions. For convenience, however, decimal mixed fractions, like simple decimal fractions, are called *decimals*.

---

141. What, then, is usually meant by the term decimal?

An expression consisting of (or containing) a fraction whose denominator is a power of ten (10, 100, 1000, etc.) and is not written below a line but indicated by numerals to the right of a point (the decimal point).

142. How is the denominational value of a decimal fraction indicated?

By the number of places to the right of the decimal point between the decimal point and the last numeral (other than 0).

143. What is the place value (fraction name) of a decimal that consists of a digit written one place to the right of the decimal point?

A tenth.

144. Give an example:

0.2   (two tenths) $(\frac{2}{10})$.

145. What is the place value of a digit two places to the right of the decimal point?

A hundredth.

EXAMPLE: 0.02   (two hundredths) $(\frac{2}{100})$.

146. Three places to the right of the decimal point?

A thousandth.

EXAMPLE: 0.002 (two thousandths) ($\frac{2}{1000}$).

---

147. Four places to the right of the decimal point?

A ten thousandth.

EXAMPLE: 0.0002 (two ten thousandths) ($\frac{2}{10.000}$).

---

148. Five places to the right of the decimal point?

A hundred thousandth.

EXAMPLE: 0.00002 (two hundred thousandths) ($\frac{2}{100.000}$).

---

149. Six places to the right of the decimal point?

A millionth.

EXAMPLE: 0.000002 (two millionths) ($\frac{2}{1.000.000}$).

---

150. How would you read a decimal having more than one digit?

Read the digits to the right of the decimal point as a whole number, but give the number the name (fraction name) of the place occupied by the last digit (other than zero).

---

151. Illustrate this rule with some examples.

Read:

0.23	twenty-three hundredths
0.234	two hundred thirty-four thousandths
0.023	twenty-three thousandths
0.0234	two hundred thirty-four ten thousandths
0.00234	two hundred thirty-four hundred thousandths
0.000234	two hundred thirty-four millionths

152. Isn't there a simpler way of reading decimals?

Yes. In shop work it is usually more convenient simply to read out the sequence of zeros and digits that follow the decimal point.

153. Give some typical examples.

Read:

0.23	point two three
0.023	point zero two three
0.000234	point zero zero zero two three four

1. 0.1 and $\frac{1}{10}$ are different expressions that have the
   _____ value.

   _____[137]

2. 0.01 if expressed as a common fraction would be
   written _____.

   _____[138]

3. Fractions of the form 0.01, 0.002, 0.0003, etc., are
   called _____ fractions, or simply _____.

   _____[139]

4. Expressions such as 2.3 and 4.6 are technically
   _____ fractions, but in ordinary language
   they are called _____, just as expressions such as
   0.1, 0.01 are also called _____.

   _____[140]

5. The denominator of a decimal fraction is not written
   as a numeral below a line; instead, it is indicated by
   numerals one or more places to the right of the
   _____ point.

   _____[141]

6. To represent a tenth decimally, we write a digit
   _____ place(s) to the right of the decimal point.

   _____[143]

7. A decimal can be defined as a common fraction whose denominator is not written and is always a power of

   _____.

   _____[141]

8. A digit written two places to the right of the decimal point has the fraction name of _____.

   _____[145]

9. Thousandths are indicated decimally by the digit _____ places to the right of the decimal point.

   _____[146]

10. Ten thousandths, hundred thousandths, and millionths are represented, respectively, by the _____,

    _____, and _____ place to the right of the decimal point.

    _____[147–149]

11. When a decimal contains more than one digit, the

    _____ digit (that is not a zero) denotes the place value (or fraction name: hundredth, thousandth, etc.) of the number.

    _____[150]

12. 0.64 is read _____.

    _____[151]

13. Sixty-four thousandths is written _____.

    _____[151]

14. 0.00234 is read _____.

    _____[151]

15. "Point zero zero two three" is an easy way of reading
    out the decimal representing _____.
    _____[153]

16. 0.000625 can be read simply as "point _____ _____
    _____ _____ _____ _____."
    _____[153]

1. Same
2. $\frac{1}{100}$
3. Decimal; decimals
4. Decimal mixed; decimals; decimals
5. Decimal
6. One
7. 10
8. A hundredth
9. Three
10. Fourth; fifth; sixth
11. Last
12. Sixty-four hundredths
13. 0.064
14. Two hundred thirty-four ten thousandths
15. Twenty-three ten thousandths
16. Zero zero zero six two five

Practice Exercise 8:
Reading and Writing Decimals

Write the names of the following decimal expressions:

1. 0.3
2. 0.7
3. 1.3
4. 2.7
5. 0.05
6. 0.15
7. 3.15
8. 0.150

9. 0.152
10. 0.052
11. 0.0152
12. 0.10037
13. 0.00137
14. 0.000017
15. 0.000137

Write the following in decimal notation:

16. Six tenths
17. Three and six tenths
18. Seven hundredths
19. Twenty-seven hundredths
20. Five thousandths
21. One hundred five thousandths
22. Six ten thousandths
23. One hundred six ten thousandths
24. Seventeen hundred thousandths
25. One hundred eighty-five millionths

1. Three tenths
2. Seven tenths
3. One and three tenths
4. Two and seven tenths
5. Five hundredths
6. Fifteen hundredths
7. Three and fifteen hundredths
8. Fifteen hundredths
9. One hundred fifty-two thousandths
10. Fifty-two thousandths
11. One hundred fifty-two ten thousandths
12. Ten thousand thirty-seven hundred thousandths
13. One hundred thirty-seven hundred thousandths
14. Seventeen millionths
15. One hundred thirty-seven millionths

16. 0.6
17. 3.6
18. 0.07
19. 0.27
20. 0.005
21. 0.105
22. 0.0006
23. 0.0106
24. 0.00017
25. 0.000185

154. What determines the denominator name (place value, such as tenths, hundredths, etc.) of a decimal fraction?

The position (place) of the last significant digit. (EXAMPLE: 0.203 is read "two hundred three thousandths," because the last significant digit, 3, is in the thousandths place.)

155. What is usually meant by the significant digits of a decimal?

The digits 1, 2, 3, 4, 5, 6, 7, 8, and 9 to the right of the decimal point, and any zeros that occur between any two of them.

156. In the decimal 0.203 is the zero to the right of the decimal point a significant digit?

Yes.

157. Why?

Because it is between 2 and 3.

158. In the decimal 0.0213 is the zero to the right of the decimal point a significant digit?

No.

159. **Why not?**

Because it does not appear between any two of the digits 1, 2, 3, 4, 5, 6, 7, 8, 9.

160. **In the decimal 0.02130, what is the first significant digit?**

2.

161. **In the decimal 0.02130, what is the last significant digit?**

3.

162. **What number is named by the decimal expression 0.6?**

Six tenths.

163. **What number is named by the decimal expression 0.60?**

Six tenths.

164. **What number is named by the decimal expression 0.600?**

Six tenths.

165. What mathematical fact is illustrated in the preceding three examples?

That writing zeros at the end of a decimal does not change the value of the decimal.

---

166. In the decimal 0.00279, what is the first significant digit?

2.

---

167. In the decimal 0.002790, what is the last significant digit?

9.

---

168. What are the significant digits in the decimal 0.0207900?

2079.

---

169. What are the significant digits in the decimal 0.0020070?

2007.

---

170. In a decimal expression such as 0.2407 is it necessary to write the zero which appears to the left of the decimal point?

No. The expression .2407 has the same value as 0.2407. The zero to the left of the decimal point is usually added, however, to help avoid errors.

---

1. The denominator name (tenths, hundredths, etc.) of a decimal fraction is determined by the position (decimal place) of the _____ significant digit.

   _____ [154]

2. The significant digits of a decimal are all the digits from _____ to _____, to the right of the decimal point, and any _____ that occur between any two of these.

   _____ [155]

3. In the decimal 0.203, the zero to the right of the decimal point is a significant digit because _____.

   _____ [156–157]

4. The zero to the right of the decimal point in 0.06195 _____ (is) (is not) a significant digit.

   _____ [158–159]

5. State the reason for your answer to the question above. _____

   _____ [159]

6. In the decimal 0.0037290, the first significant digit is

   _____.

   _____ [160]

7. In the decimal 0.0037290, the last significant digit is

   _____.

   _____ [161]

8. Write $\frac{6}{10}$ in decimal form. _____
_____ [162]

9. What number is named by the expression 0.30?

_____

_____ [163]

10. The number represented by 0.300 is _____.

_____ [164]

11. Zeros placed at the end of a decimal _____ the value of the decimal.

_____ [165]

12. The significant digits in the decimal 0.0017060 are

_____.

_____ [168]

13. _____ are the significant digits in the expression 0.000340002900.

_____ [169]

14. In expressions such as 0.2407, the zero to the left of the decimal point is not _____, but is usually written to help avoid errors.

_____ [170]

1. Last
2. 1; 9; zeros
3. It occurs between the digits 2 and 3.
4. Is not
5. Because it does not lie between any two of the digits 1–9
6. 3
7. 9
8. 0.6
9. Three tenths
10. Three tenths
11. Do not change
12. 1706
13. 3400029
14. Required (or, necessary)

CHANGING FRACTIONS TO DECIMALS AND DECIMALS TO FRACTIONS

---

171. Can every proper fraction be written as an equivalent decimal?

Yes.

---

172. How do we find the decimal equivalent of a proper fraction?

By dividing the denominator into the numerator.

---

173. Show this in an example.

To change $\frac{1}{4}$ to an equivalent decimal: Divide 1 by 4:

$$4\overline{)1.00} \quad = .25 \ \textit{Ans.}$$

---

174. What is the decimal equivalent of $\frac{3}{8}$?

$$\begin{array}{r} .375 \quad \textit{Ans.} \\ 8\overline{)3.000} \end{array}$$

---

175. What happens when we change $\frac{1}{3}$ to a decimal expression?

$$\begin{array}{r} .333333\cdots \quad \textit{Ans.} \\ 3\overline{)1.000000\cdots} \end{array}$$

We obtain the expression $0.333333\cdots$, which is a nonterminating decimal in which the sequence of digits keeps repeating.

---

176. Give some other examples of fractions whose decimal expression does not terminate.

$$\frac{1}{6} = 0.16666\cdots$$
$$\frac{5}{11} = 0.454545\cdots$$
$$\frac{2}{3} = 0.666666\cdots$$

---

177. What fact does the repetitions in the preceding examples indicate?

That although every proper fraction can be expressed decimally, many fractions cannot be expressed as terminating (or finite) decimals.

---

178. Can every terminating decimal be expressed as a fraction?

Yes.

---

179. How do we find the fractional equivalent of a decimal?

We write the significant digits of the decimal (in their proper order) as the numerator of the fraction. The number denominator is indicated by the place value of the last significant digit. The fraction thus obtained can then, if desired, be rewritten in its simplest form (reduced to lowest terms).

180. Change 0.125 to an equivalent fraction.

Significant digits: 125
Place value of last significant digit: thousandths.

$$\frac{125}{1000} \quad (\text{or } \frac{1}{8})$$

181. Change 0.09375 to an equivalent fraction.

Significant digits: 9375
Place value of last significant digit: hundred thousandths.

$$\frac{9375}{100,000} \quad (\text{or } \frac{3}{32})$$

1. Every proper fraction can be written as an _____ decimal.

   _____[171]

2. To change a proper fraction to a decimal, we _____ the _____ into the _____.

   _____[172]

3. $\frac{1}{4}$ expressed decimally is _____.

   _____[173]

4. 0.75 is the decimal equivalent of _____.

   _____[173–174]

5. When certain fractions, such as $\frac{1}{3}$ and $\frac{1}{6}$, are expressed decimally, the result is a _____ decimal.

   _____[175–176]

6. Although every proper fraction can be expressed decimally, many fractions cannot be expressed as _____ decimals.

   _____[177]

7. To find the fractional equivalent of a decimal, we write the significant digits of the decimal as the

   _____. The _____ is indicated by the _____ of the last significant digit.

   _____[179]

1. Equivalent
2. Divide; denominator; numerator
3. 0.25
4. $\frac{3}{4}$

5. Nonterminating (or, repeating)
6. Terminating (or, finite)
7. Numerator; denominator; place value

ADDITION AND
SUBTRACTION OF DECIMALS

182. How can we add 21.34 and 2.04?

The same way we add $21.34 and $2.04.

```
21.34
 2.04
23.38
```

183. Add 60.03, 72.1, and .0004.

```
 60.03
 72.1
   .0004
132.1304
```

184. What general rule can we derive from the preceding operations?

To add decimals, we place the numbers in a column, but keep the decimal points directly under the decimal point at the top of the column. We then proceed as with whole numbers. The decimal point in the answer is placed under the decimal points in the numbers added.

185. Does the same principle (relative to the decimal point) apply in the subtraction of mixed decimals?

It does.

186. Subtract 5.01 from 36.12.

$$\begin{array}{r} 36.12 \\ 5.01 \\ \hline 31.11 \end{array}$$

187. Subtract .037 from 21.009.

$$\begin{array}{r} 21.009 \\ .037 \\ \hline 20.972 \end{array}$$

188. What is the difference in value between 36.12 and 36.120?

None. The value of a decimal is not changed if zeros are added at the right. The place value is determined by the last significant digit.

189. Why is this fact important?

It is convenient when subtracting a decimal (or a number containing a decimal) from one that has fewer places (to the right of the decimal point) to annex zeros to the one with fewer places—providing both numbers with the same number of places.

190. Show this in some examples.

Subtract 3.117 from 36.12.

$$\begin{array}{r} 36.120 \\ 3.117 \\ \hline 33.003 \end{array}$$

Subtract .00072 from 36.1.

$$\begin{array}{r} 36.10000 \\ .00072 \\ \hline 36.09928 \end{array}$$

Subtract 1.017 from 36.

$$\begin{array}{r} 36.000 \\ 1.017 \\ \hline 34.983 \end{array}$$

1. In adding decimals, we place the numbers in a column, but keep the _____ directly under each other (except, obviously, the _____ in the number at the top of the column.

   _____[184]

2. The decimal point in the sum is located directly _____ the _____ in the numbers to be added.

   _____[184]

3. In subtracting one decimal from another, the decimal point is placed in the same relative position as in _____ decimals.

   _____[185]

4. The value of a decimal is _____ if zeros are added to the right of the significant digits.

   _____[188]

5. When subtracting a decimal from one that has fewer places to the right of the decimal point, it is helpful to _____ to the number that has fewer places.

   _____[189]

6. If we are to subtract 3.117 from 36.12, it is convenient to write 36.12 as _____.

   _____[190]

1. Decimal points; decimal point
2. Under; decimal point
3. Adding
4. Not changed
5. Annex zeros
6. 36.120

Practice Exercise 9: Addition and Subtraction of Decimals

Add the following decimals as indicated:

1. $3.475 + 7.307 + 0.009 + 0.382$
2. $0.982 + 2.008 + 1.404 + 0.265$
3. $0.97 + 4.25 + 35.58 + 66.98$
4. $0.61 + 0.03 + 0.72 + 0.98$
5. $17.009 + 179.453 + 0.086 + 2.535$
6. $62.2 + 927.5 + 10.0 + 86.4$

Subtract the following decimals as indicated:

7. $237.5 - 217.9$
8. $37.702 - 27.692$
9. $200.25 - 50.75$
10. $2.06 - 0.581$
11. $9.0004 - 7.1596$
12. $0.405 - 0.17923$

1. 11.173
2. 4.659
3. 107.78
4. 2.34
5. 199.083
6. 1086.1
7. 19.6
8. 10.01
9. 149.5
10. 1.479
11. 1.8408
12. 0.22577

MULTIPLICATION OF DECIMALS

191. Rewrite $\frac{1}{2} \times \frac{1}{2} = \frac{1}{4}$ in decimal form.

$0.5 \times 0.5 = 0.25.$

192. Rewrite $\frac{1}{4} \times \frac{3}{2} = \frac{3}{8}$ in decimal form.

$0.25 \times 1.5 = 0.375.$

193. What do you find to be the same and what do you find to be different in the relation of the sentence $0.5 \times 0.5 = 0.25$ to the sentence $5 \times 5 = 25$, and in the relation of the sentence $0.25 \times 1.5 = 0.375$ to the sentence $25 \times 15 = 375$?

In both cases the digits are the same; only the position of the decimal point is different.

194. Multiply 0.255 by 0.05.

$$\begin{array}{r} 0.255 \\ \underline{0.05} \\ 0.01275 \end{array}$$

---

195. What principle is illustrated in the preceding examples?

That to multiply decimals we operate as we would in multiplying whole numbers. The only difference lies in the placing of a decimal point.

---

196. How was the position of the decimal point indicated in the preceding examples?

The number of places to the right of the decimal point in the product was equal to the sum of the decimal places in the multiplier and the number multiplied (multiplicand).

---

197. Put this rule in simpler language.

To find the number of places to the right of the decimal point in the product, add the number of places in the multiplier and the number of places in the number multiplied.

---

198. If the multiplier has two places to the right of the decimal point and the number multiplied also has two places to the right of the decimal point, how many places are to be pointed off in the product?

Four.

---

199. If the multiplier has two decimal places and the number multiplied three decimal places, how many decimal places will there be in the product?

Five.

200. Is there any easy way to multiply a decimal by 10, 100, 1000 and any higher power of ten?

Yes. We simply move the decimal point to the right as many places as there are zeros in the multiplier.

201. Show this in some examples.

$$0.232 \times 10 \quad = \quad 2.32$$
$$0.232 \times 100 \quad = \quad 23.2$$
$$0.232 \times 1000 \quad = \quad 232.$$
$$0.232 \times 10000 = 2320.$$

202. What do we do when the multiplier is 0.1, 0.01, 0.001, etc.?

Move the decimal point to the *left* as many places as there are decimal places (including the 1) in the multiplier.

203. Show this in some examples.

$$232.5 \times 0.1 \quad = 23.25$$
$$232.5 \times 0.01 \quad = \quad 2.325$$
$$232.5 \times 0.001 \quad = \quad 0.2325$$
$$232.5 \times 0.0001 = \quad 0.02325$$

1. Decimals are multiplied in the same way as whole numbers except for the fact that the position of the _____ must be determined.

   _____[195]

2. When decimals are multiplied, the number of decimal places in the product is equal to the _____ of the decimal places in the _____ and the

   _____.

   _____[196]

3. Four places are to be pointed off in the product if the _____ has two places and the _____ has _____ places.

   _____[198]

4. If the first number (in the above case) has three decimal places, and the other, two, the product will have _____ decimal places.

   _____[199]

5. To multiply a decimal by any power of 10 (100, 1000, etc.), we simply move the decimal point to the right as many _____ as there are _____ in the multiplier.

   _____[200]

6. $0.232 \times 100 =$ _____.

   _____[201]

7. If we want to multiply a decimal by 0.1, 0.01, 0.001 (or any other negative power of 10), we move the decimal point of the decimal to the _____ as many places as there are decimal places in the multiplier.

_____[202]

8. 232.5 × 0.01 = _____.

_____[203]

Practice Exercise 10:
Multiplication of Decimals

Find the following products:

1. 0.2×0.3
2. 3.7×0.02
3. 0.45×0.7
4. 0.05×1000
5. 6.5×0.1
6. 0.01×6.5
7. 0.001×6.5
8. 5.5×3.3
9. 7.85×6.66
10. 0.85×0.6
11. 5.4×0.0073
12. 83.2×0.059
13. 854.4×0.67
14. 0.0002×0.00000023

1. Decimal point
2. Sum; multiplier; number multiplied (or, multiplicand). The last two answers can be exchanged
3. Multiplier; number multiplied (or in reverse order); two
4. Five
5. Places; zeros
6. 23.2
7. Left
8. 2.325

ANSWERS: PRACTICE EXERCISE 10

1. 0.06
2. 0.074
3. 0.315
4. 50
5. 0.65
6. 0.065
7. 0.0065
8. 18.15
9. 52.281
10. 0.51
11. 0.03942
12. 4.9088
13. 572.448
14. 0.000000000046

DIVISION OF DECIMALS

---

204. **What is the easiest way to divide a decimal by a whole number?**

Proceed as you would with whole numbers, but place the decimal point in the quotient directly above the decimal point in the number to be divided.

---

205. **Show this in an example.**

Divide 0.36 by 6.

$$6 \overline{)0.36} \quad \begin{array}{c} 0.06 \end{array} \quad Ans.$$

---

206. Divide 0.036 by 6.

$$6 \overline{)\ 0.036} = 0.006 \quad \textit{Ans.}$$

207. Divide 0.0288 by 32.

$$32 \overline{)\ 0.0288} = 0.0009 \quad \textit{Ans.}$$
$$\underline{288}$$

208. What is the easiest way to divide a whole number by a decimal?

Apply the identity principle (which states, as we have seen, that multiplying any number by 1 leaves the number unchanged) to rewrite the statement of the required operation as a division of one whole number by another. (Remember 1 can be written as $\frac{10}{10}$, $\frac{100}{100}$, $\frac{1000}{1000}$, etc.)

209. Show this in an example.

EXAMPLE: To divide 35 by 0.07.

$$35 \div 0.07 = \frac{35}{0.07} = \frac{35 \times 100}{0.07 \times 100} = \frac{3500}{7}$$
$$= 500$$

210. Divide 144 by 0.006.

$$\frac{144}{0.006} = \frac{144 \times 1000}{0.006 \times 1000} = \frac{144{,}000}{6}$$
$$= 24{,}000$$

211. What principle is involved when we move a decimal point to the right, or annex zeros to a whole number?

Moving a decimal point to the right is equivalent to multiplying the decimal by 10 or some power of 10. Annexing zeros to a whole number is equivalent to multiplying the whole number by 10 or some power of 10.

212. Isn't the value of a number changed when we multiply it by 10?

Of course. But as we have already seen, in our discussions of equivalent fractions (Frames 48–58), if we multiply both the numerator and denominator of a fraction (that is, a dividend and a divisor) by the same number, the quotient is unchanged because we are multiplying the fraction by 1. This is the meaning of the identity principle, as we have seen.

213. Show this with fractions.

$$\frac{2}{4} = \frac{1}{2}$$

$$\frac{2 \times 2}{2 \times 4} = \frac{4}{8} = \frac{1}{2}$$

$$\frac{3 \times 2}{3 \times 4} = \frac{6}{12} = \frac{1}{2}$$

$$\frac{5 \times 2}{5 \times 4} = \frac{10}{20} = \frac{1}{2}$$

214. Show this with decimals.

$$\frac{10 \times 0.2}{10 \times 0.4} = \frac{2}{4} = 0.5$$

$$\frac{100 \times 0.2}{100 \times 0.4} = \frac{20}{40} = 0.5$$

$$\frac{1000 \times 0.2}{1000 \times 0.4} = \frac{200}{400} = 0.5$$

215. Summing up these basic principles, what can we say is the general rule for dividing by decimals?

Applying the identity principle, multiply both divisor and dividend by the power of 10 (10, 100, 1000, 10,000, etc.) that will express the divisor as a whole number. Carry out the division as with whole numbers.

216. Divide 0.81 by 0.03.

$$0.81 \div 0.03 = 81 \div 3 = 3\overline{)81}^{27} \qquad Ans.$$

217. Divide 0.028 by 0.007.

$$0.028 \div 0.007 = 28 \div 7 = 7\overline{)28}^{4} \qquad Ans.$$

218. Divide 0.150 by 0.0005.

$$0.150 \div 0.0005 = 1500 \div 5 = 5\overline{)1500}^{300} \qquad Ans.$$

219. Divide 0.003 by 0.6.

$$0.003 \div 0.6 = 0.03 \div 6 = 6\overline{)0.030} \quad \overset{0.005}{} \quad Ans.$$

---

220. Divide 25.5 by 0.05.

$$25.5 \div 0.05 = 2550 \div 5 = 5\overline{)2550} \quad \overset{510}{} \quad Ans.$$

---

221. Divide 7.80 by 2.6.

$$7.80 \div 2.6 = 78 \div 26 = 26\overline{)78} \quad \overset{3}{} \quad Ans.$$

---

222. When dividing decimals (as sometimes with whole numbers), the quotient can be extended indefinitely. To how many places should it be carried?

There is no rule for this. Obviously, the more places in your answer, the greater the accuracy of the answer. Usually four or five places is sufficient. (NOTE: Four places to the right of the decimal point gives a reading in ten thousandths; five places, in hundred thousandths.)

1. To divide a decimal by a whole number, we proceed
   as we would in dividing one whole number by another

   ... but we locate the decimal point of the _____

   directly _____ the decimal point in the

   _____.

   _____[204]

2. $0.36 \div 6 =$ _____.

   _____[205]

3. $0.036 \div 6 =$ _____.

   _____[206]

4. $0.0288 \div 32 =$ _____.

   _____[207]

5. The easiest way to divide a whole number by a deci-

   mal is to apply the _____ principle, which enables

   us to rewrite the problem as a division of one _____
   number by another.

   _____[208]

6. 1 can be rewritten as $\dfrac{?}{10}$, $\dfrac{100}{?}$, or $\dfrac{?}{1000}$

   _____[208]

7. $\dfrac{35 \times 100}{0.07 \times 100} = ?$

   _____[209]

8. $\dfrac{144 \times 1000}{0.006 \times 1000} = ?$

_____[210]

9. In a decimal, if we move the decimal point one place to the right, the number obtained is the same as that obtained by multiplying the decimal by _____.

_____[211]

10. If we annex one zero to a whole number, the number thus obtained is the same as that obtained if the whole number was multiplied by _____.

_____[211]

11. We have already discovered that the value of a fraction is not changed if we multiply both the _____ and the denominator by _____ number.

_____[212]

12. In general, if division is to be performed with a decimal as the divisor, it is helpful to rewrite the problem in such a way as to make the divisor a _____.

_____[215]

13. In a division involving decimals, if the quotient is not exact (that is, is a continuing decimal), it is usually sufficient to carry it out to _____ places (unless greater precision is required).

_____[222]

Practice Exercise 11: Division of Decimals

Carry out answer (if necessary) to three decimal places.

1. $23.5 \div 16$
2. $2.743 \div 77$
3. $32 \overline{)5.372}$

4. $5.0832 \div 51$
5. $\dfrac{0.0765}{23}$
6. $4.2768 \div 8$

Carry out answer (if necessary) to four decimal places.

7. $\dfrac{0.02958}{12}$
8. $30.625 \div 3.5$
9. $0.36 \overline{)0.045}$
10. $0.0059 \overline{)0.034456}$

11. $5.368848 \div 0.6$
12. $0.000576 \div 0.008$
13. $5.64852 \div 0.457$
14. $\dfrac{4610}{0.875}$

1. Quotient; Above; number to be divided (or, dividend)
2. 0.06
3. 0.006
4. 0.0009
5. Identity; whole
6. 10; 100; 1000
7. $\frac{3500}{7}$ (or 500)
8. $\frac{144,000}{6}$ (or 24,000)
9. 10
10. 10
11. Numerator; the same
12. Whole number
13. Four or five

ANSWERS: PRACTICE EXERCISE 11

1. 1.469
2. 0.036
3. 0.168
4. 0.100
5. 0.003
6. 0.535
7. 0.002465
8. 8.75
9. 0.125
10. 5.84
11. 8.9481
12. 0.072
13. 12.36
14. 5269